CONTENTS

Published by

WARNER BROS. PUBLICATIONS INC.
265 Secaucus Road • Secaucus, N.J. 07096-2037
A Warner Communications Company

Exclusive Distributor

P.O. BOX 27 New Berlin, WI 53151

ANGEL

CLARINET
FULL 'N' MELLOW
Medium ROCK or DISCO

Words and Music by
MADONNA CICCONE and STEVE BRAY

3

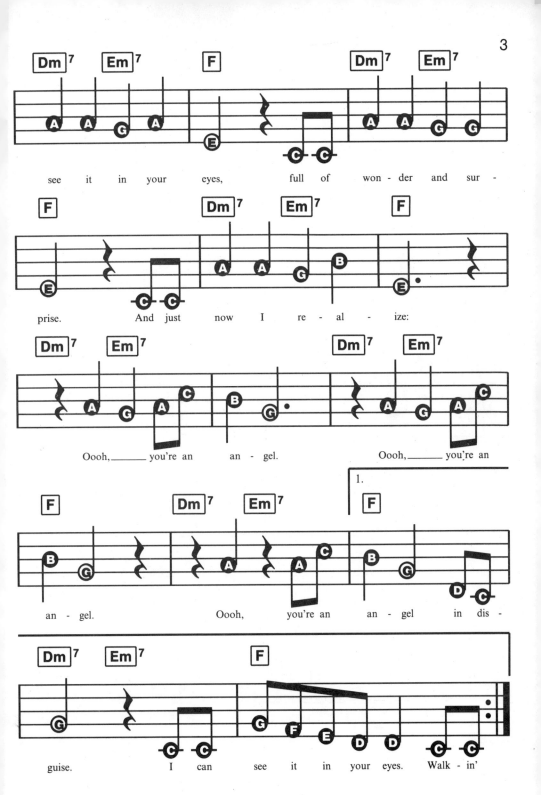

4

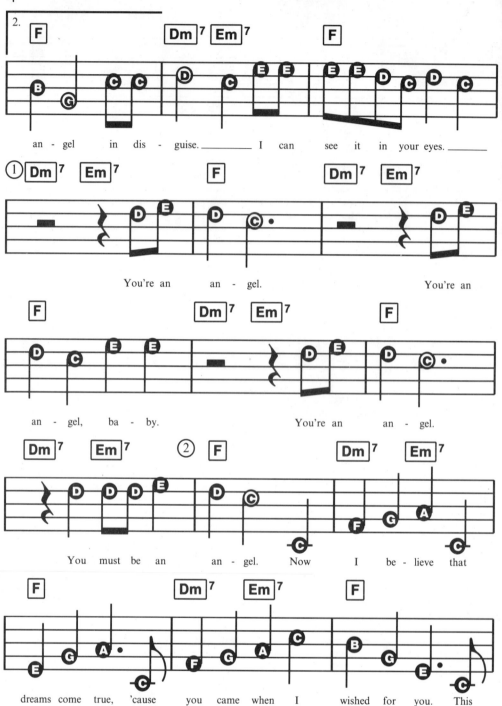

2. F   Dm⁷   Em⁷   F

an - gel   in   dis - guise. _____ I   can   see   it   in   your eyes. _____

① Dm⁷   Em⁷   F   Dm⁷   Em⁷

You're an   an - gel.   You're an

F   Dm⁷   Em⁷   F

an - gel,   ba - by.   You're an   an - gel.

Dm⁷   Em⁷   ② F   Dm⁷   Em⁷

You   must   be   an   an - gel.   Now   I   be - lieve   that

F   Dm⁷   Em⁷   F

dreams come   true,   'cause   you   came   when   I   wished   for   you.   This

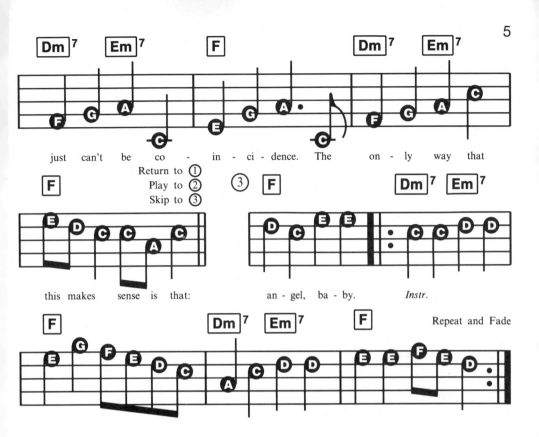

CAUSING A COMMOTION

SAXOPHONE
BIG 'N' BOLD
Medium ROCK

Words and Music by
MADONNA CICCONE and STEVE BRAY

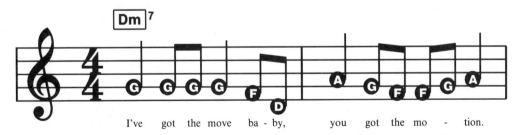

6

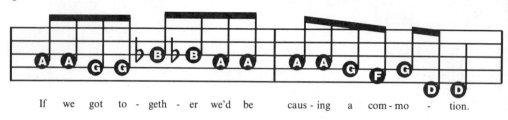

If we got to-geth-er we'd be caus-ing a com-mo - tion.

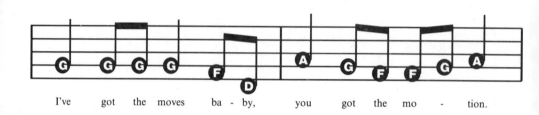

I've got the moves ba - by, you got the mo - tion.

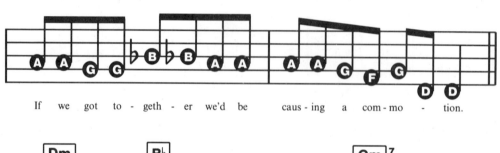

If we got to-geth - er we'd be caus-ing a com-mo - tion.

You met your match when you met me, _____
Some - day you'll see my point of view, _____

_____ I know that you will dis - a - gree, it's cra - zy.
_____ you can't keep wish - ing on the stars _____ ba - by.

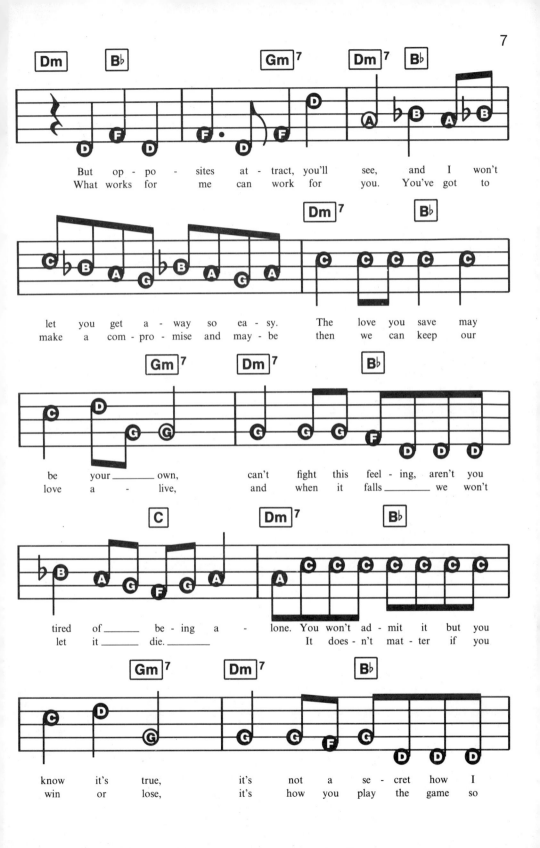

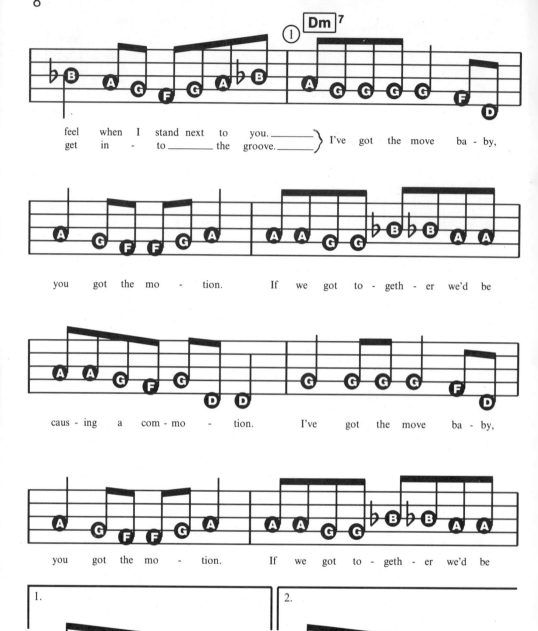

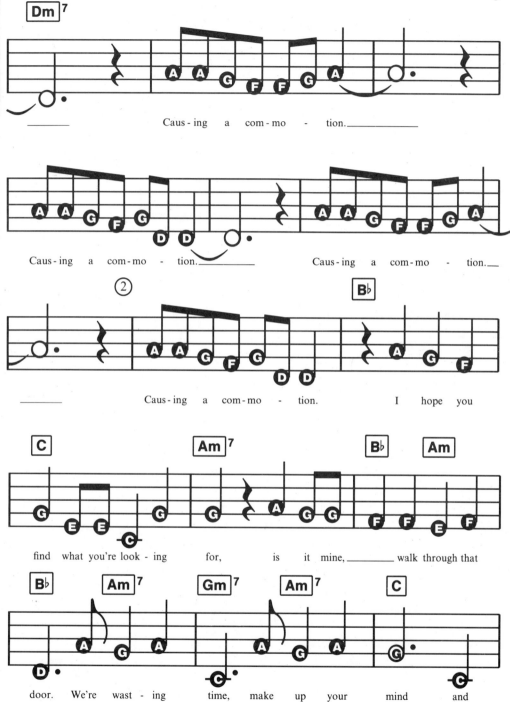

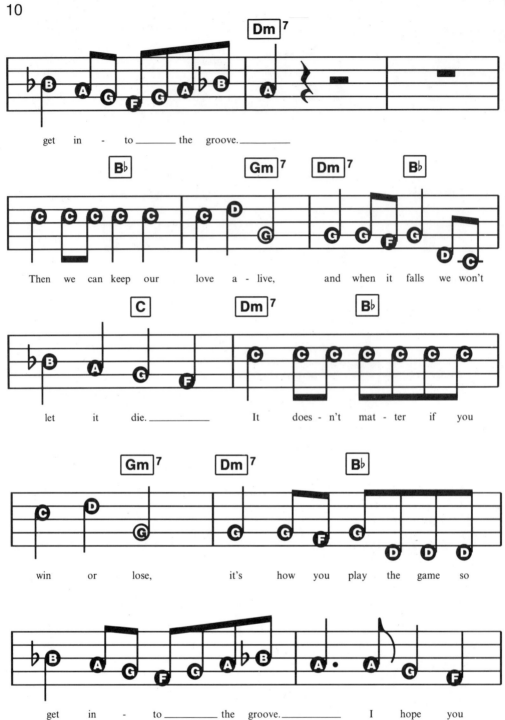

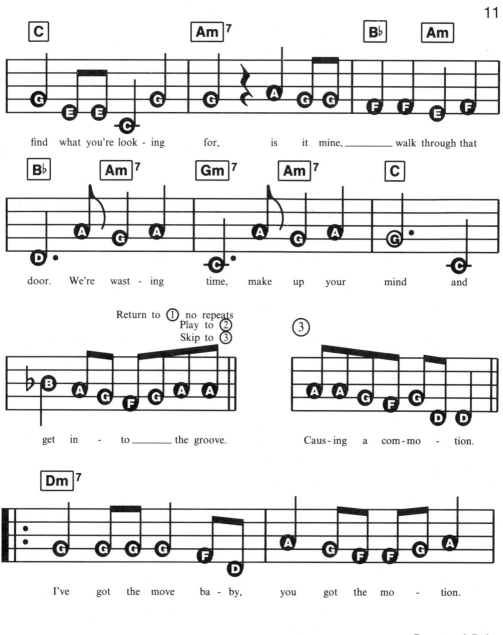

DRESS YOU UP

FLUTE
BIG 'N' BOLD
Medium ROCK

Words and Music by
PEGGY STANZIALE and ANDREA LaRUSSO

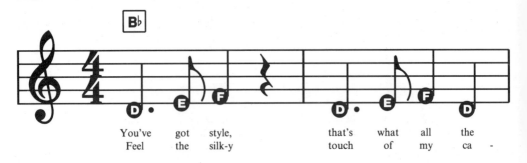

You've got style, that's what all the
Feel the silk-y touch of my ca -

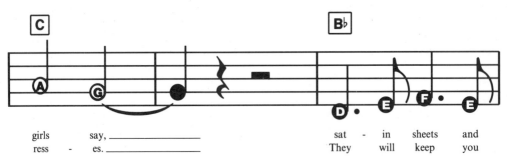

girls say, _____ sat - in sheets and
ress - es. _____ They will keep you

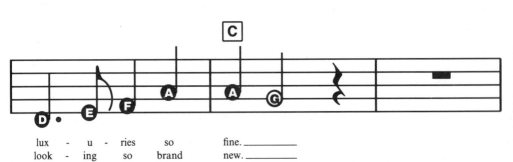

lux - u - ries so fine. _____
look - ing so brand new. _____

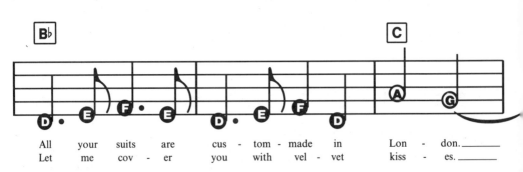

All your suits are cus - tom - made in Lon - don. _____
Let me cov - er you with vel - vet kiss - es. _____

13

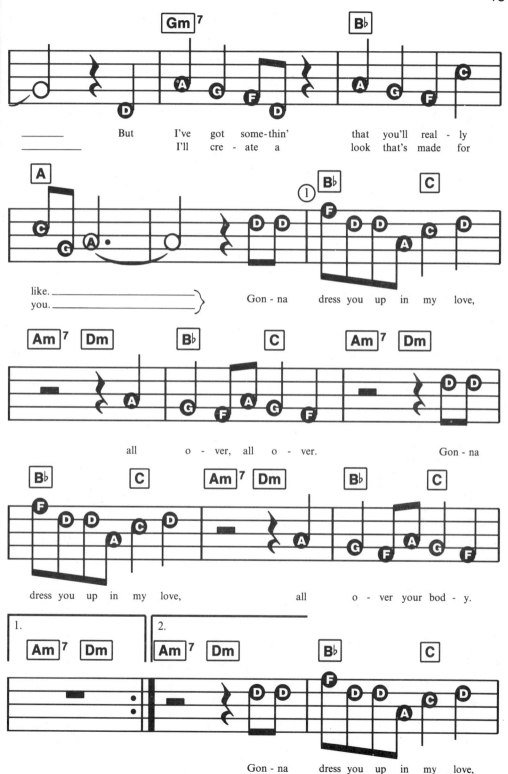

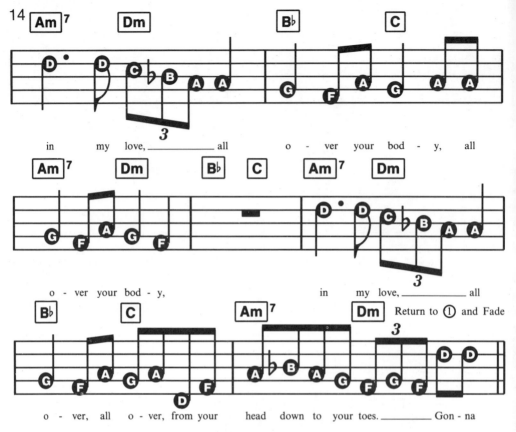

in my love, _____ all o - ver your bod - y, all

o - ver your bod - y, in my love, _____ all

o - ver, all o - ver, from your head down to your toes. _____ Gon - na

HOLIDAY

CLARINET
BIG 'N' BRIGHT
Medium ROCK or DISCO

Words and Music by
LISA STEVENS and CURTIS HUDSON

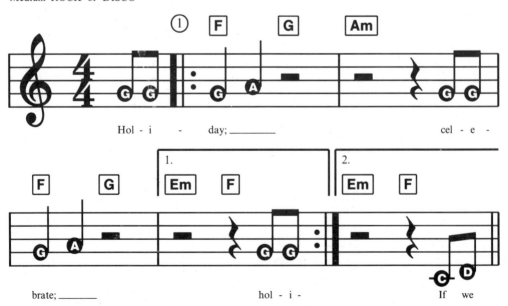

Hol - i - day; _____ cel - e -

brate; _____ hol - i - If we

took a hol - i - day, _____ took some

time to cel - e - brate. _____ Just one

day out of life; it would be, _____ it would

be so nice. { Ev - ery - bod - y spread the word, _____ we're
{ You can turn this world a - round, _____ and

gon - na have a cel - e - bra - tion, all a - cross the
bring back all of those hap - py days. Put your trou- ble

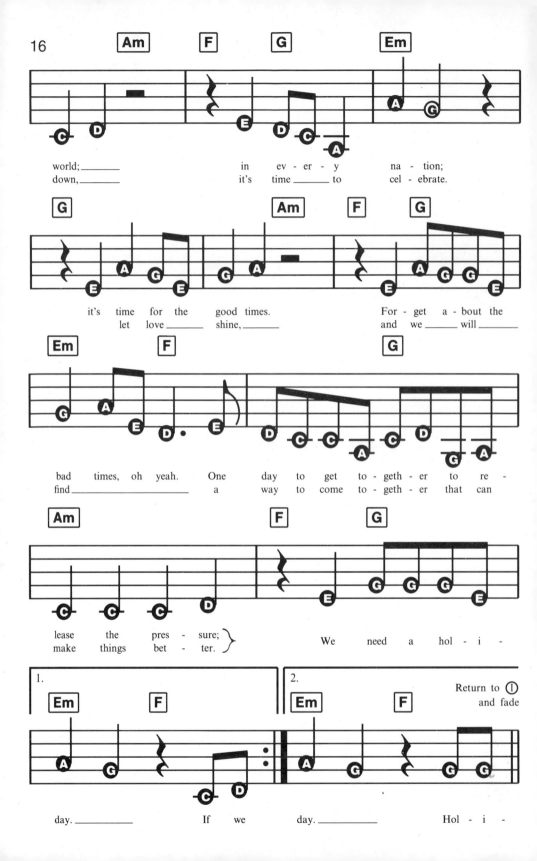

BORDERLINE

CLARINET
BIG 'N' BOLD
Medium ROCK

Words and Music by
REGGIE LUCAS

Some-thing in the way you love me won't let me
Some-thing in your eyes is mak - ing such a fool of

be; _____
me; _____

I don't want to be your bus - 'ness, so
when you hold me in your arms, you

ba - by won't you set me free. _____ Stop
love me till I just can't see. _____ But,

play - in' with my heart; fin - ish what you start;
then you let me down; when I look a - round,

well, you make my love come down. If you
ba - by you just can't be found. Stop

want me let me know; ba - by let it show;
driv - in' me a - way, I just want to stay;

hon - ey don't you fool a - round.
some-thing I just got to say. Just

try to un - der - stand, I've giv - en all I

can; 'cause you've got the best of me.

Chorus

Bor - der - line; feels like I'm

19

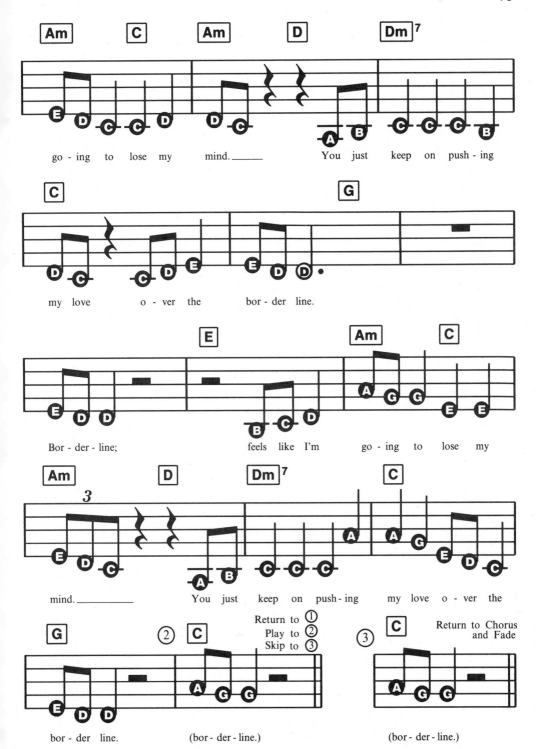

INTO THE GROOVE

TRUMPET
BRIGHT 'N' BRASSY
Medium ROCK or DISCO

Words and Music by
MADONNA CICCONE and STEVE BRAY

Get in-to the groove. Boy, you've got to prove your love to me. Yeah, _____ get up on your

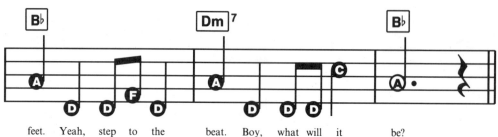

feet. Yeah, step to the beat. Boy, what will it be?

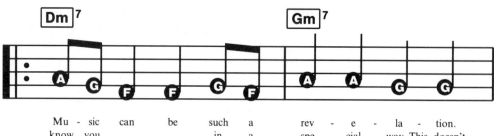

Mu - sic can be such a rev - e - la - tion.
know you in a spe - cial way. This doesn't

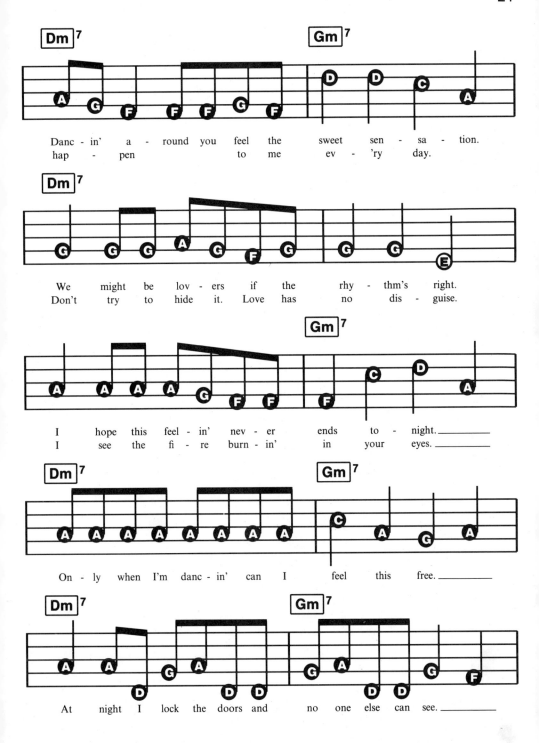

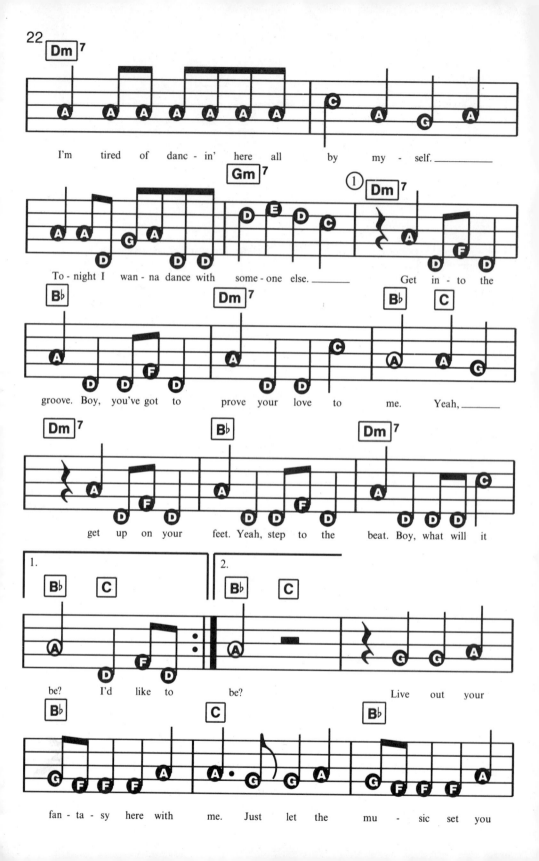

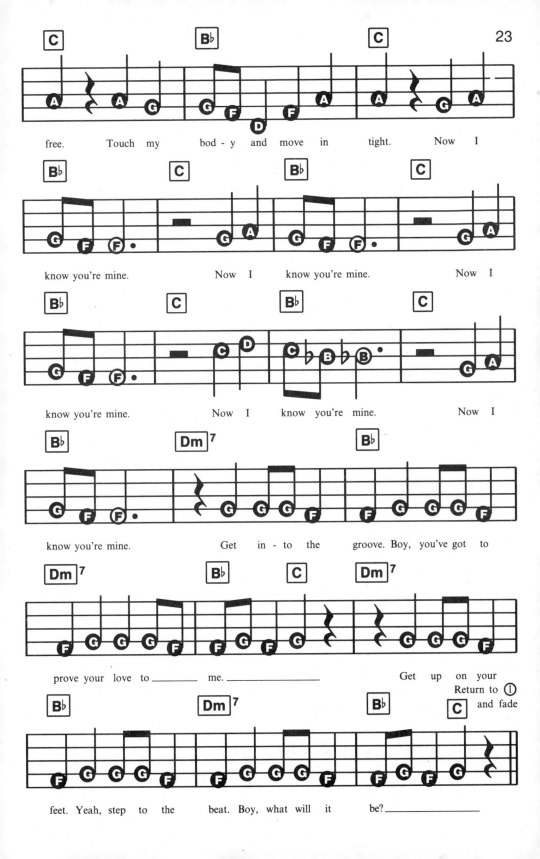

24

LA ISLA BONITA

SAXOPHONE
BIG 'N' BOLD
Medium DISCO

Words and Music by
MADONNA CICCONE, PAT LEONARD
and BRUCE GEITCH

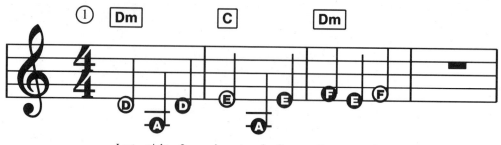

Last night I dreamt of San Pe - dro,
I fell in love with San Pe - dro,
girl. *(Instrumental)*

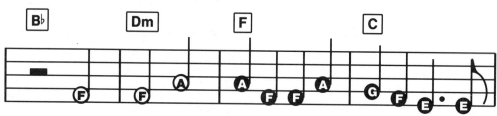

just like I'd nev - er gone. I knew the song, a
warm wind carried on the sea. He called to me,

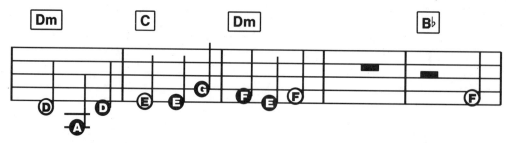

young girl with eyes like the des - ert. It
Te di - so te am - o. I
Last night I dreamt of San Pe - dro. It

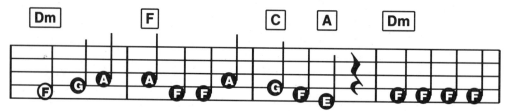

all seems like yes - ter - day, not far a - way.
prayed that the days would last, they went so fast. Trop - i - cal the
all seems like yes - ter - day, not far a - way.

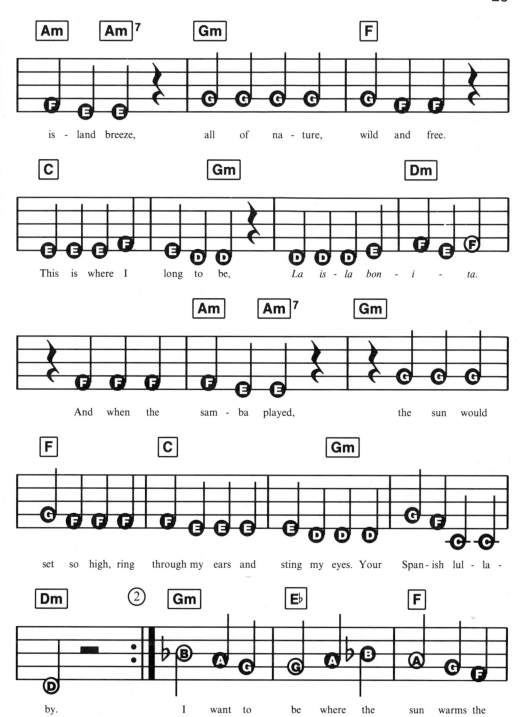

26

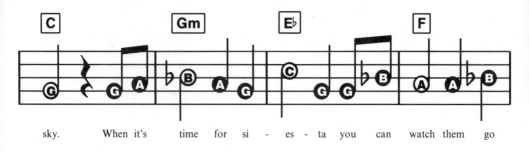

sky. When it's time for si - es - ta you can watch them go

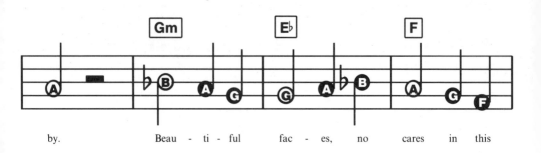

by. Beau - ti - ful fac - es, no cares in this

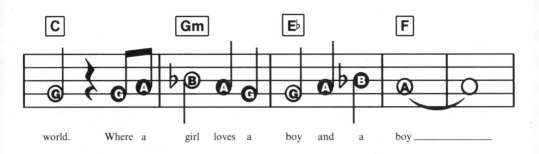

world. Where a girl loves a boy and a boy_____

Return to ①
Play to ②
Skip to ③

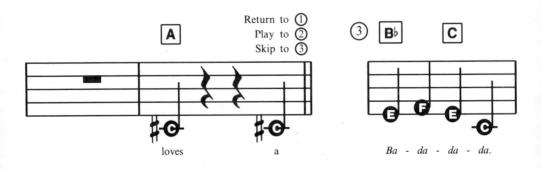

loves a

Ba - da - da - da.

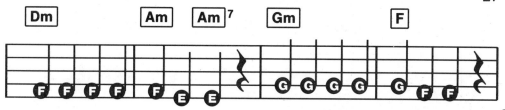

Trop - i - cal the is - land breeze, all of na - ture, wild and free.

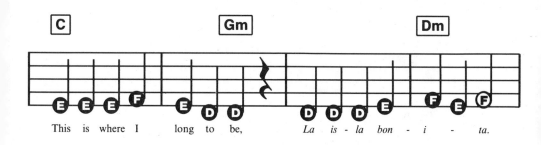

This is where I long to be, *La is - la bon - i - ta.*

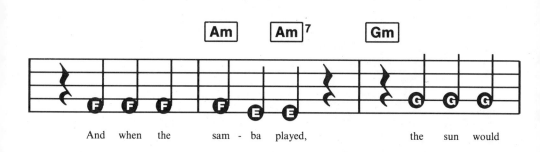

And when the sam - ba played, the sun would

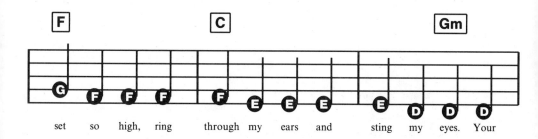

set so high, ring through my ears and sting my eyes. Your

28

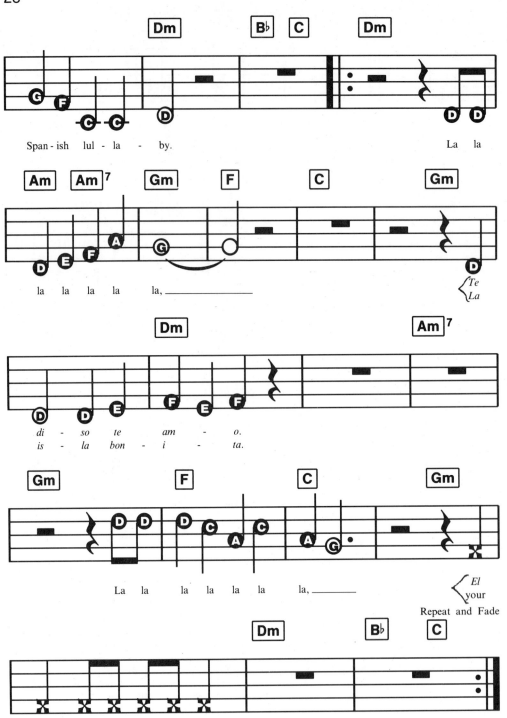

Span - ish lul - la - by.   La   la

la   la   la   la   la, _____   Te
                                                                         La

di – so te   am – o.
is – la bon – i – ta.

La   la   la   la   la   la   la, _____   El
                                                                        your
                                                            Repeat and Fade

di – jo que te - am - a.
Span - ish lul – la - by.

CRAZY FOR YOU

FLUTE
FULL 'N' MELLOW
Slow ROCK

Words and Music by
JOHN BETTIS and JON LIND

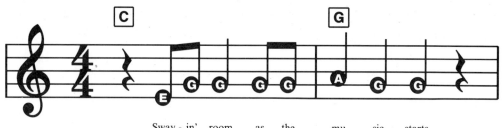

Sway - in' room   as   the   mu - sic   starts.
Try - in' hard   to   con - trol   my   heart,

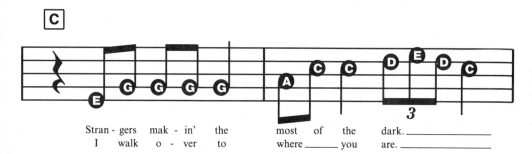

Stran - gers   mak - in'   the   most   of   the   dark._____
I   walk   o - ver   to   where_____ you   are. _____

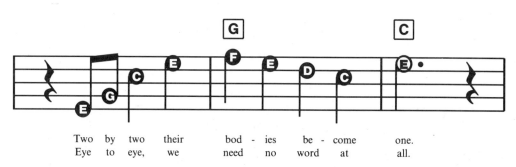

Two   by   two   their   bod - ies   be - come   one.
Eye   to   eye,   we   need   no   word   at   all.

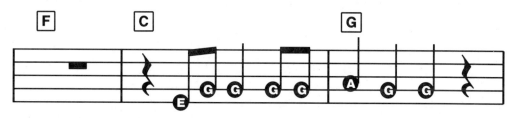

I   see   you   through the   smok - y   air.
Slow - ly   now   we   be - gin   to   move.

Can't you feel the weight of my stare. _____
Ev - 'ry breath I'm deeper in - to you. _____

You're so close, but still a world a - way. _____ What I'm
Soon we two are stand - in' still in time. _____ If you

dy - in' to say: You bet I'm ⎞
read my ____ mind, you'll see I'm ⎠ cra - zy for you.

Touch ____ me once ____ and you'll know it's true. I nev - er want - ed an - y -

one like this. It's all brand ____ new. You'll feel it in my kiss. _____

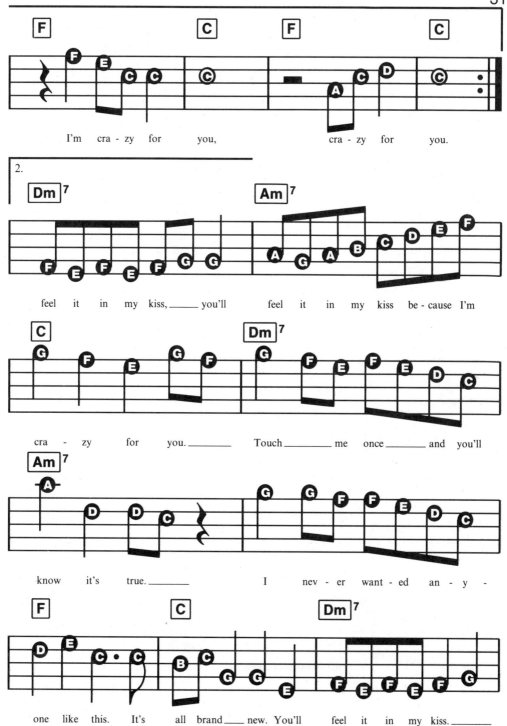

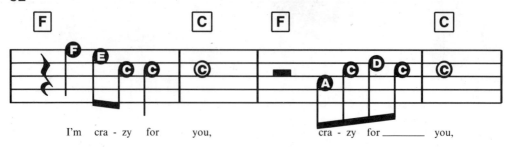

I'm cra - zy for you, cra - zy for _____ you,

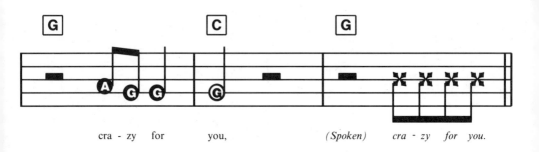

cra - zy for you, *(Spoken)* cra - zy for you.

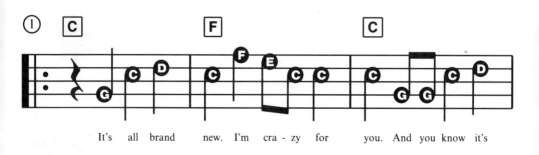

It's all brand new. I'm cra - zy for you. And you know it's

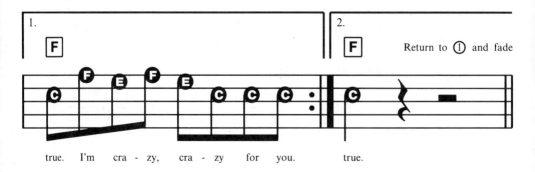

true. I'm cra - zy, cra - zy for you. true.

LIKE A VIRGIN

ORGAN
BIG 'N' BOLD
Medium ROCK or DISCO

Words and Music by
BILLY STEINBERG and TOM KELLY

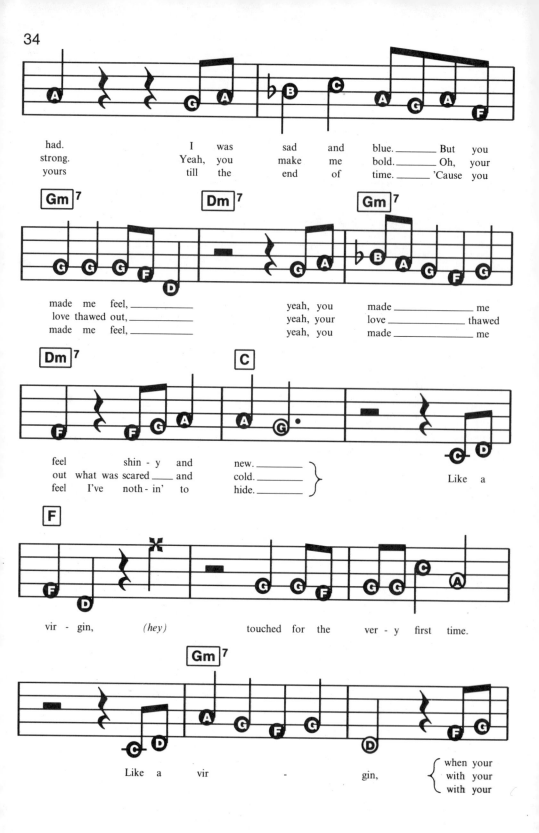

vir - gin.   Ooh, _____ ooh, _____ like a

vir - gin.   Feels so good___ in - side _____ when you

Repeat and Fade

hold me   and your   heart beats   and you   love me.

LIVE TO TELL

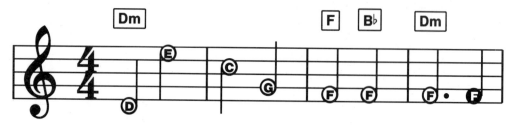

TRUMPET
FULL 'N' MELLOW
Medium ROCK

Words and Music by
MADONNA CICCONE and PAT LEONARD

I
I

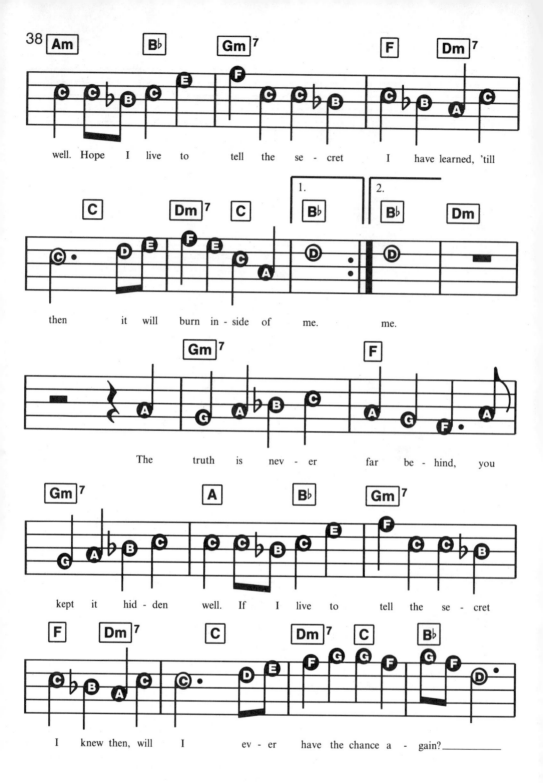

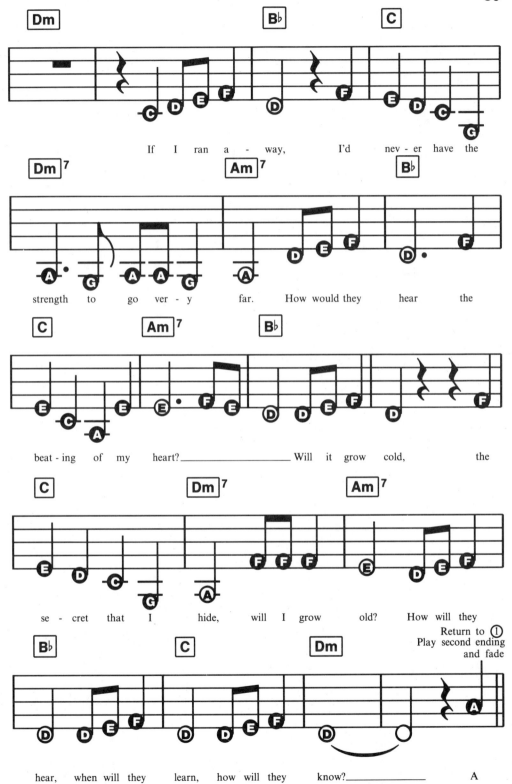

WHO'S THAT GIRL?

TRUMPET
FULL 'N' MELLOW
Medium ROCK or DISCO

Words and Music by
MADONNA CICCONE and PATRICK LEONARD

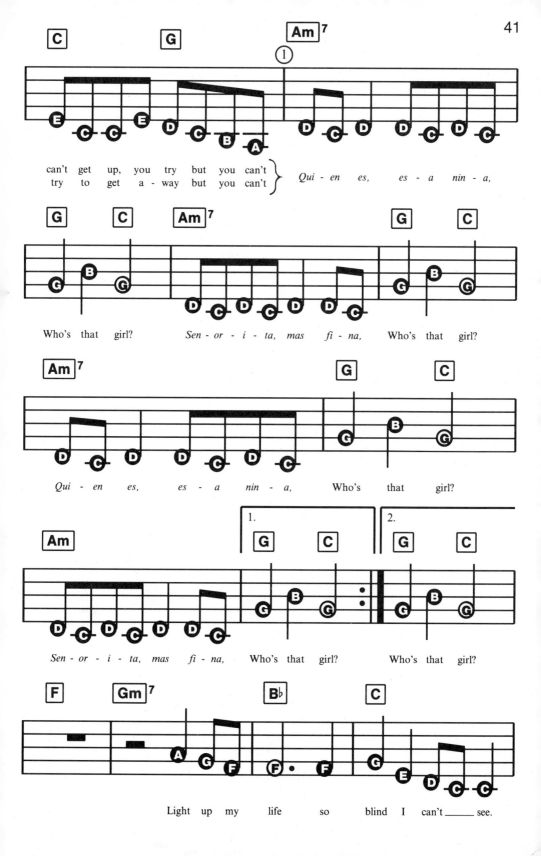

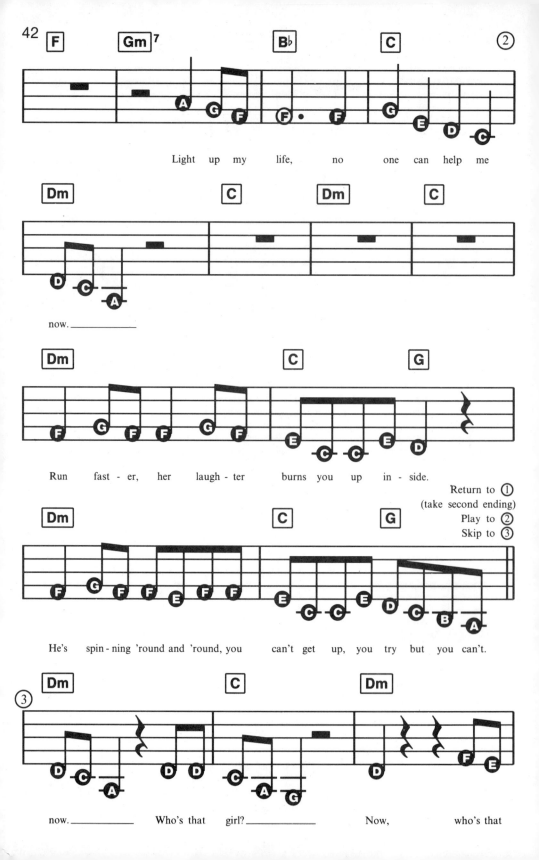

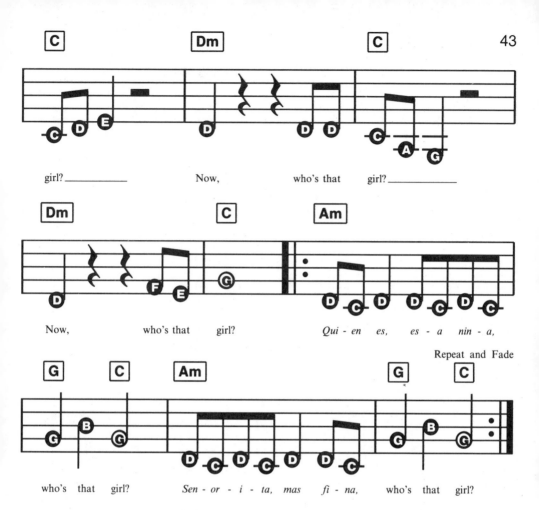

girl? _____ Now, who's that girl? _____

Now, who's that girl? *Qui - en es, es - a nin - a,*

Repeat and Fade

who's that girl? *Sen - or - i - ta, mas fi - na,* who's that girl?

LUCKY STAR

ORGAN
BIG 'N' BRIGHT
Medium ROCK or DISCO

Words and Music by
MADONNA CICCONE

You must be my luck - y star, _____ 'cause you
You must be my luck - y star, _____ 'cause you

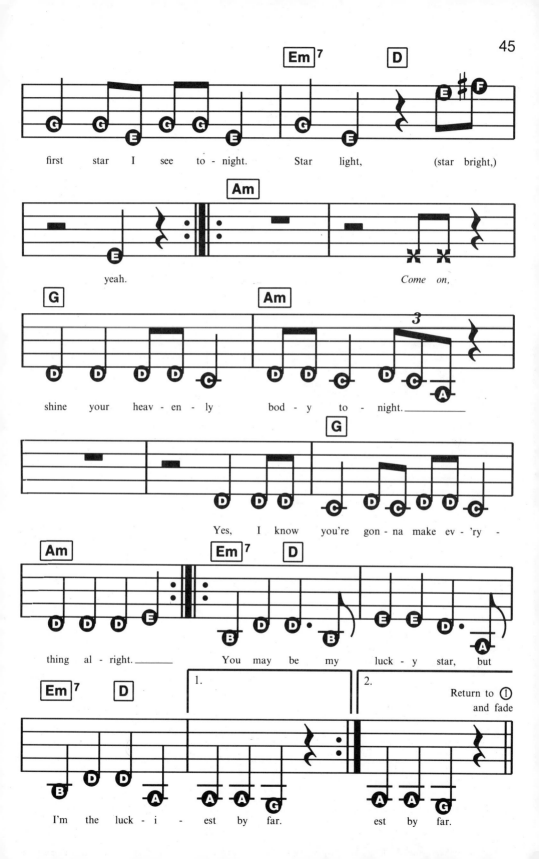

OPEN YOUR HEART

TRUMPET
BIG 'N' BOLD
Medium ROCK

Words and Music by
MADONNA CICCONE, GARDNER COLE
and PETER RAFELSON

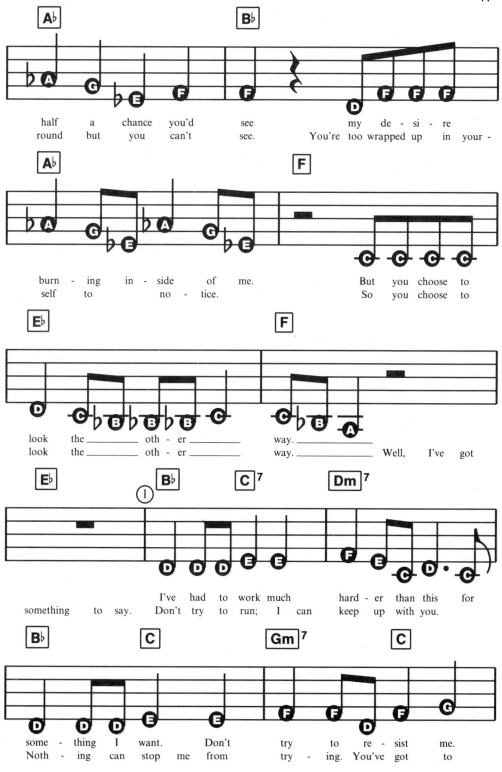

48

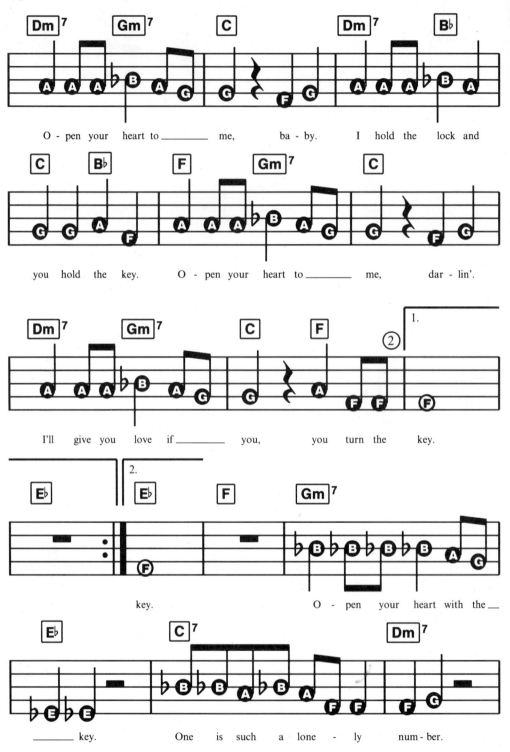

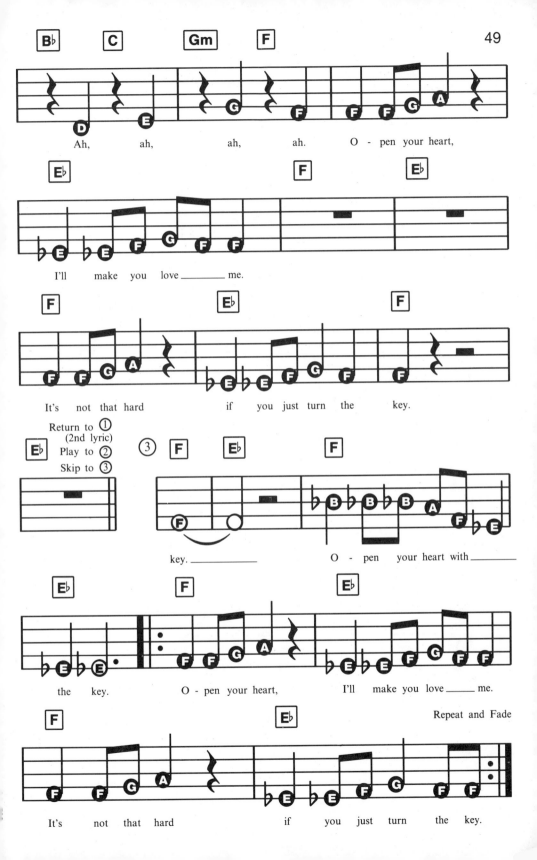

50

PAPA DON'T PREACH

SAXOPHONE
BIG 'N' BOLD
Medium ROCK

Words and Music by
BRIAN ELLIOT

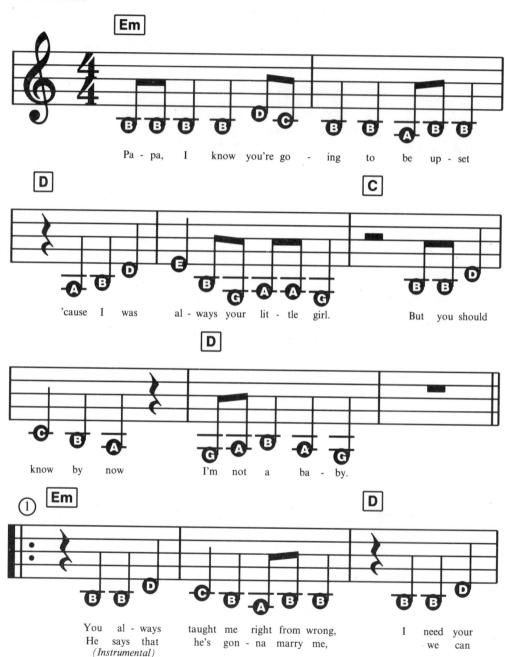

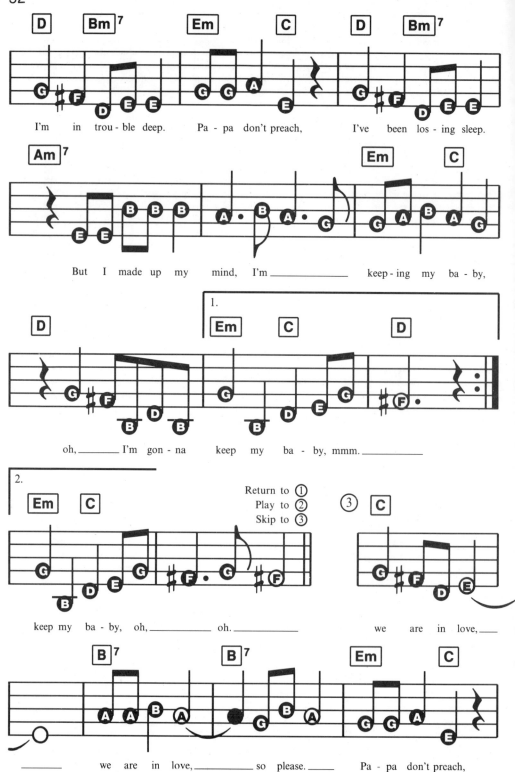

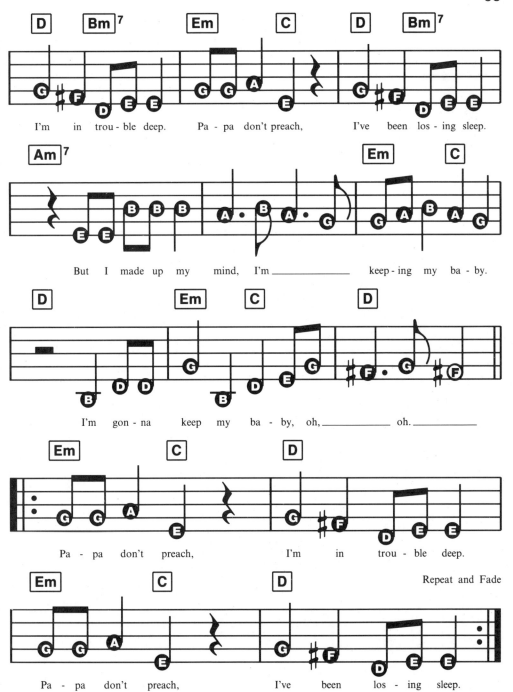

54

TRUE BLUE

ORGAN
SOFT SOLO
Medium SWING

Words and Music by
MADONNA CICCONE and STEVE BRAY

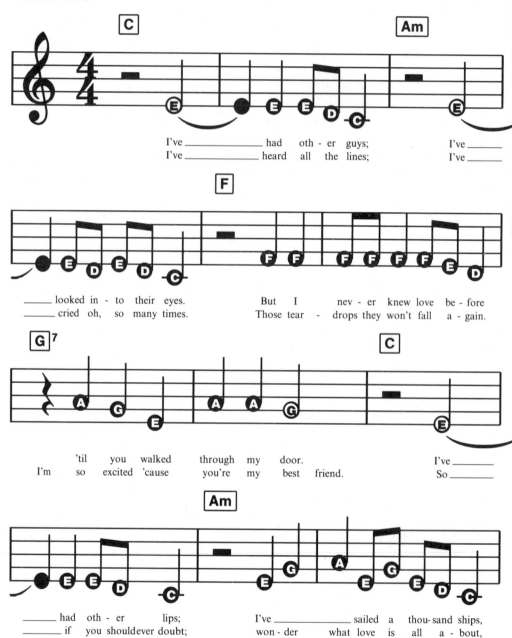

I've _____ had oth - er guys; I've _____
I've _____ heard all the lines; I've _____

_____ looked in - to their eyes. But I nev - er knew love be - fore
_____ cried oh, so many times. Those tear - drops they won't fall a - gain.

'til you walked through my door. I've _____
I'm so excited 'cause you're my best friend. So _____

_____ had oth - er lips; I've _____ sailed a thou-sand ships,
_____ if you shouldever doubt; won - der what love is all a - bout,

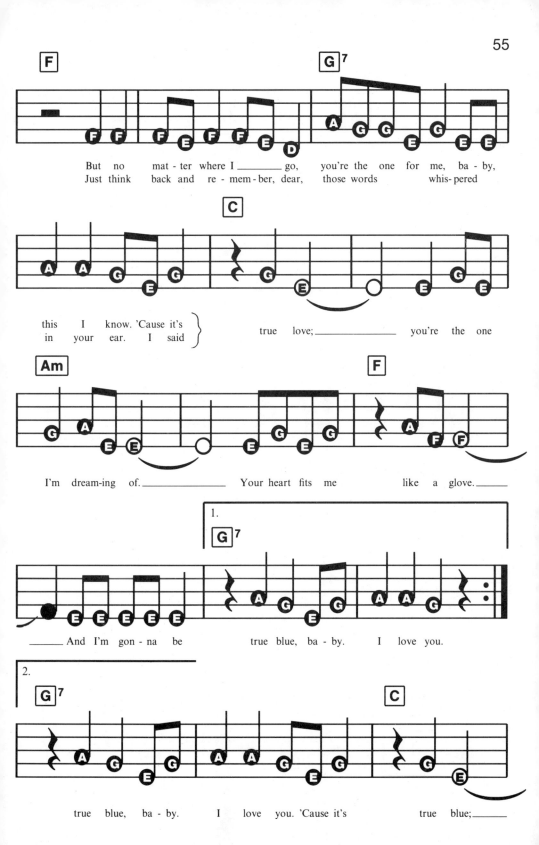

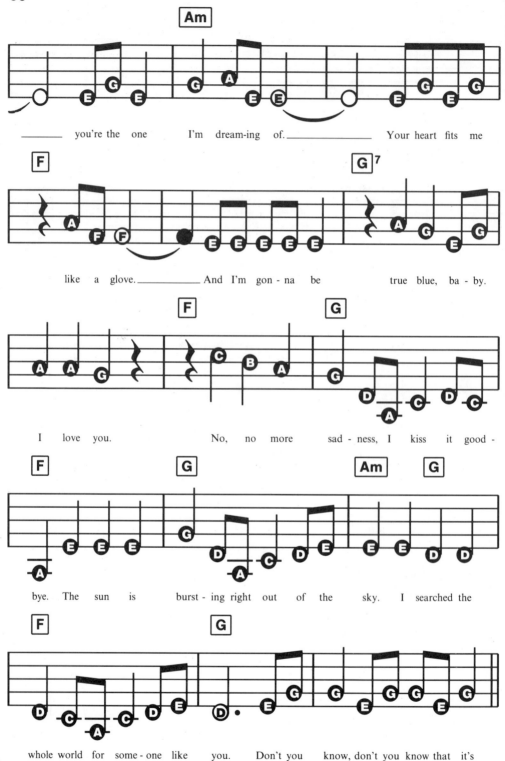

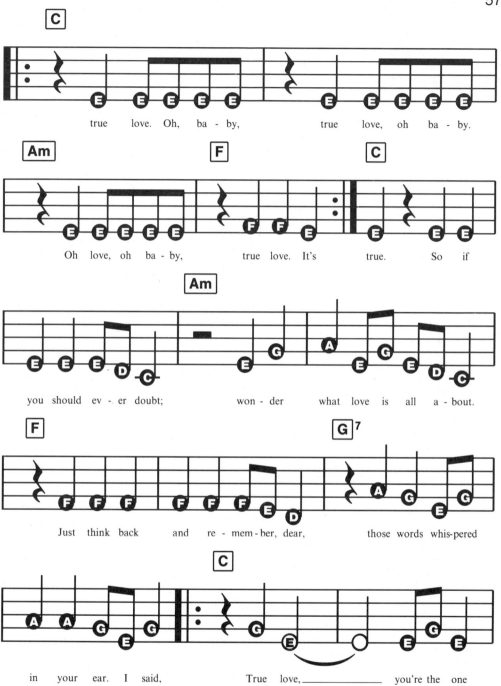

I'm dream-ing of._____ Your heart fits me like a glove._____

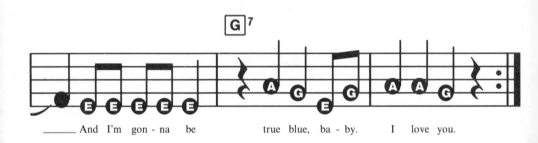

_____ And I'm gon - na be true blue, ba - by. I love you.

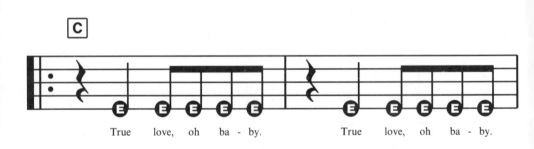

True love, oh ba - by. True love, oh ba - by.

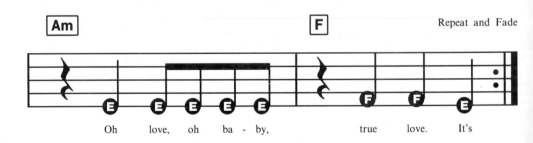

Repeat and Fade

Oh love, oh ba - by, true love. It's

MATERIAL GIRL

TRUMPET
BRIGHT 'N' BRASSY
Medium ROCK or DISCO

Words by PETER BROWN and ROBERT RAINS
Music by PETER BROWN

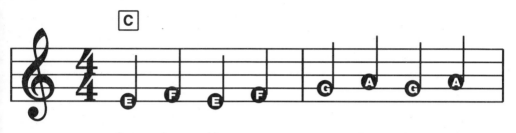

Some boys kiss me, some boys hug me.
Some boys ro - mance, some boys slow dance.

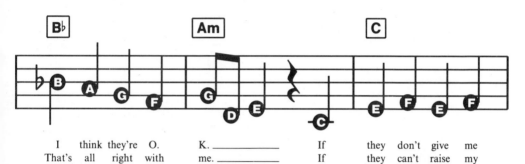

I think they're O. K. _____ If they don't give me
That's all right with me. _____ If they can't raise my

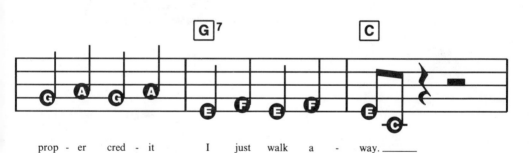

prop - er cred - it I just walk a - way. _____
in - t'rest then I have to let them be. _____

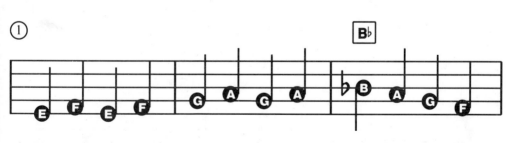

They can beg and they can plead but they can't see the
Some boys try and some boys lie but I don't let them
Boys may come and boys may go and that's all right, you

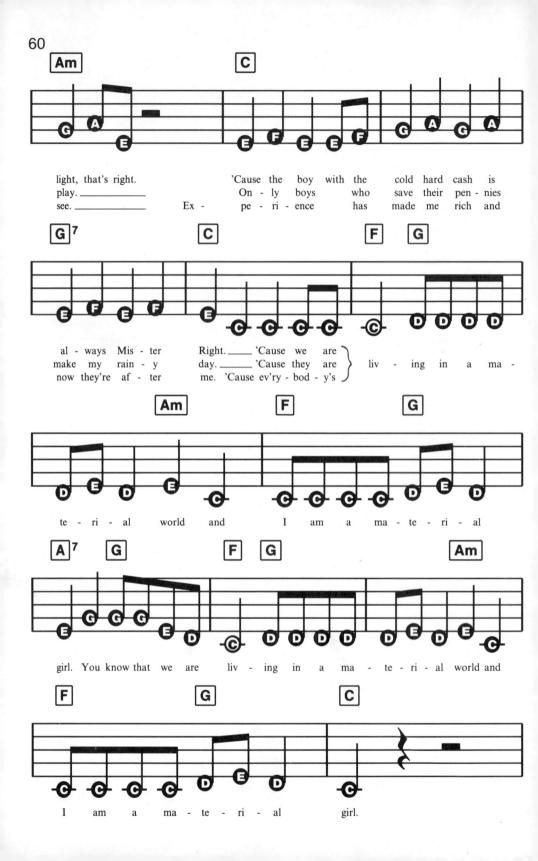

Am · C

light, that's right.   'Cause the boy with the cold hard cash is
play.＿＿＿   On - ly boys who save their pen - nies
see.＿＿＿   Ex - pe - ri - ence has made me rich and

G⁷ · C · F · G

al - ways Mis - ter Right.＿ 'Cause we are ⎫
make my rain - y day.＿ 'Cause they are ⎬ liv - ing in a ma -
now they're af - ter me. 'Cause ev'ry - bod - y's ⎭

Am · F · G

te - ri - al world and   I am a ma - te - ri - al

A⁷ · G · F · G · Am

girl. You know that we are liv - ing in a ma - te - ri - al world and

F · G · C

I am a ma - te - ri - al girl.

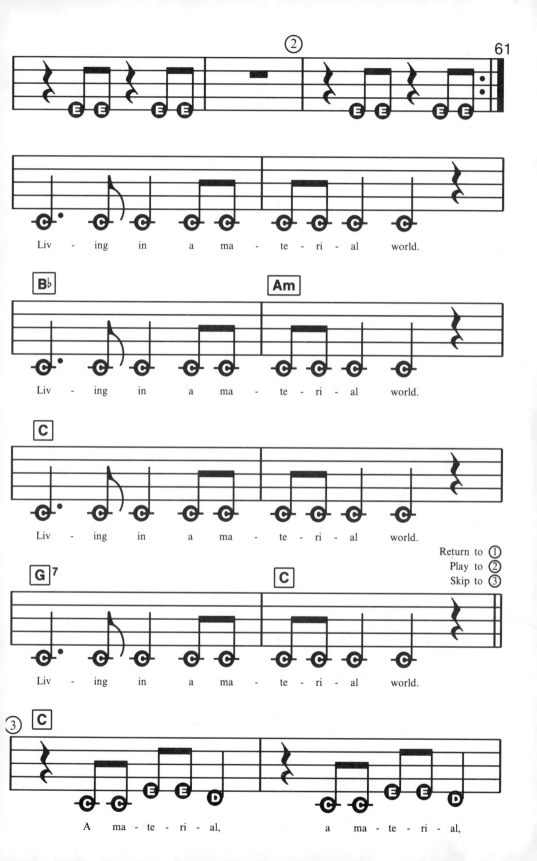

Living in a material world.

B♭   **Am**

Living in a material world.

C

Living in a material world.

Return to ①
Play to ②
Skip to ③

G⁷   **C**

Living in a material world.

③ **C**

A ma - te - ri - al,   a ma - te - ri - al,

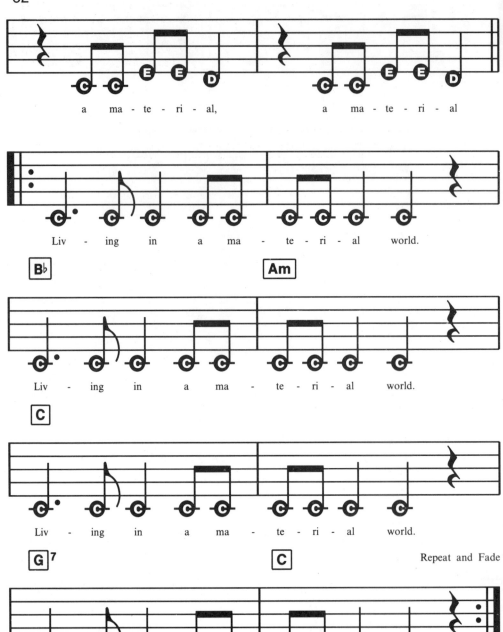

a ma - te - ri - al,   a ma - te - ri - al

Liv - ing in a ma - te - ri - al world.

B♭   **Am**

Liv - ing in a ma - te - ri - al world.

C

Liv - ing in a ma - te - ri - al world.

G⁷   **C**   Repeat and Fade

Liv - ing in a ma - te - ri - al world.

THE ABC's OF

The Melody
(Right Hand)

The melody appears as large lettered notes. The letter name corresponds to a key on your keyboard.

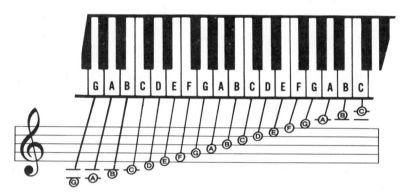

Sharps and Flats

In LETTER MUSIC a **sharp** (♯) tells you to play the very next key to the right and a **flat** (♭) tells you to play the very next key to the left. These are black keys. Notes without a **sharp** (♯) or **flat** (♭) are white keys.

Ties

A **tie** is a curved line connecting notes on the same line or in the same space. It indicates the first note is struck and then held for the total time value of the tied notes. Only notes with a letter inside are struck.

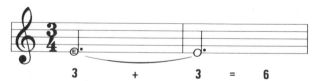

3   +   3   =   6

The Accompaniment
(Left Hand)

The accompaniment consists of chords. All the major and minor chords you need to play appear inside a box. Optional seventh (7) chords appear outside the box.

C   G⁷   Cm   Gm⁷

N.C. tells you "No Chord" is played — just the right-hand melody.

Generally, there are three ways to play chords: One finger, traditional, and three-note Easy-Play chords. Your owner's guide can help you decide which methods your keyboard is capable of. Be sure to try them all.

MUSIC BASICS

The Staff, Measures and Bar Lines

The **staff** consists of five lines and four spaces and each is named with one of the letters A through G. Any note that appears on one of the lines or in one of the spaces is called by that letter-name.

The S-shaped symbol at the beginning of the staff is called the **treble clef** and tells you all the notes that follow are to be played by your right hand.

The staff is divided into equal sections by using vertical lines called **bar lines**. The sections between the bar lines are called **measures**.

Time Values

In music, time is measured in **beats**. The illustration shows the types of notes you'll play and how many beats each type gets.

Rests are shown in the lower part of the illustration, along with the number of beats each type gets. A rest indicates a period of silence, when you don't play — they still must be counted, however.

Time Signature

The two numbers at the beginning of a song are known as the **time signature**. The top number indicates the number of beats in each measure. The bottom number 4 tells you each quarter note (♩) receives one beat.

Repeat Signs and Double Endings

These tell you to play certain parts of a song more than once.

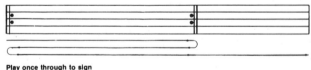

Play once through to sign
Go back to other sign or beginning of song
And play a second time.   If more music — keep going.

Sometimes a repeated song, or part of a song, has two different endings. In these cases, **double endings** are used.

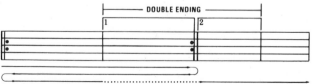

Play first time using first ending.
Go back to other sign or beginning,
Play second time —   (skip first ending)   play second ending.
                                                          If more music — keep going.